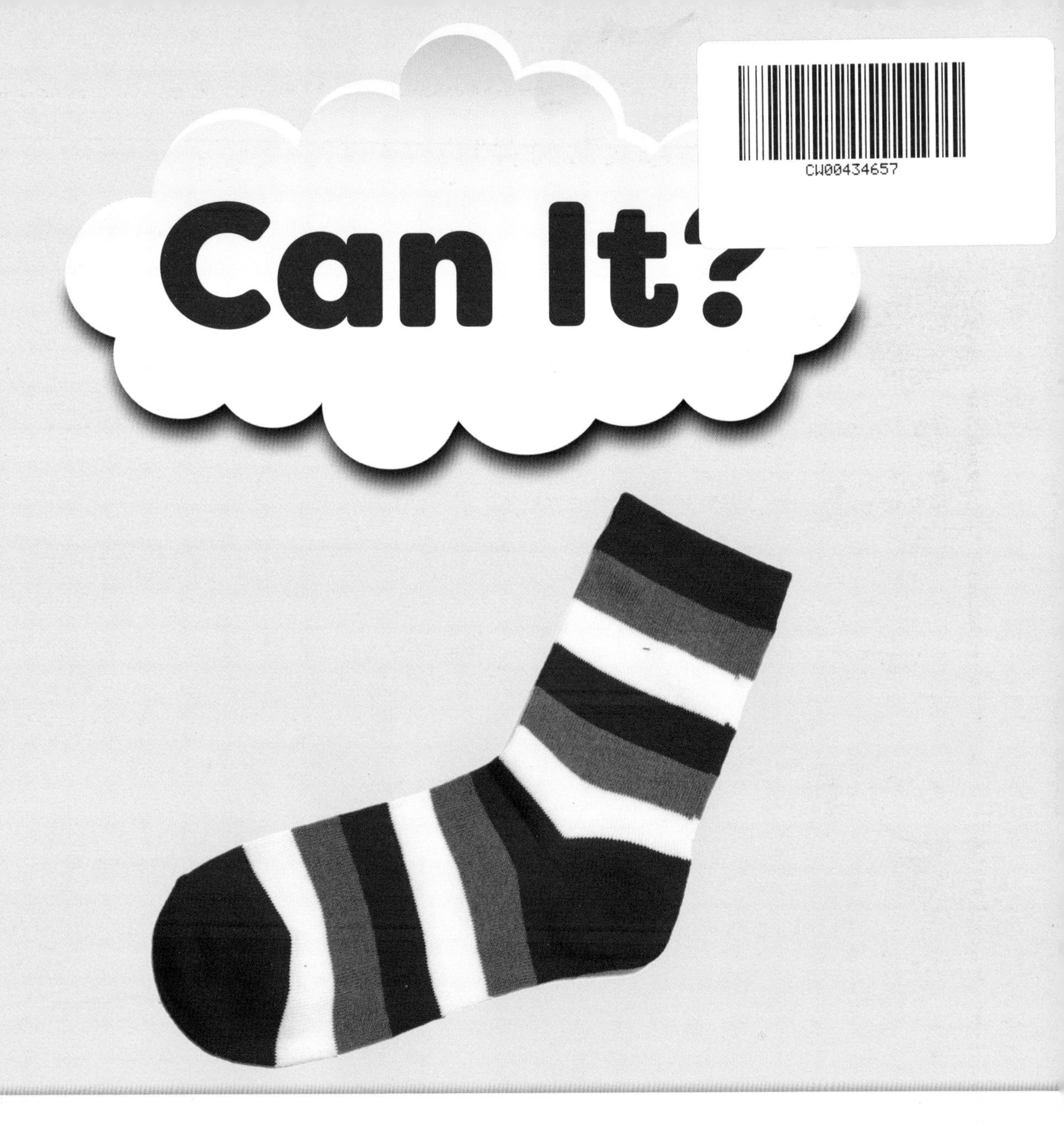

Written by Debbie Vilardi

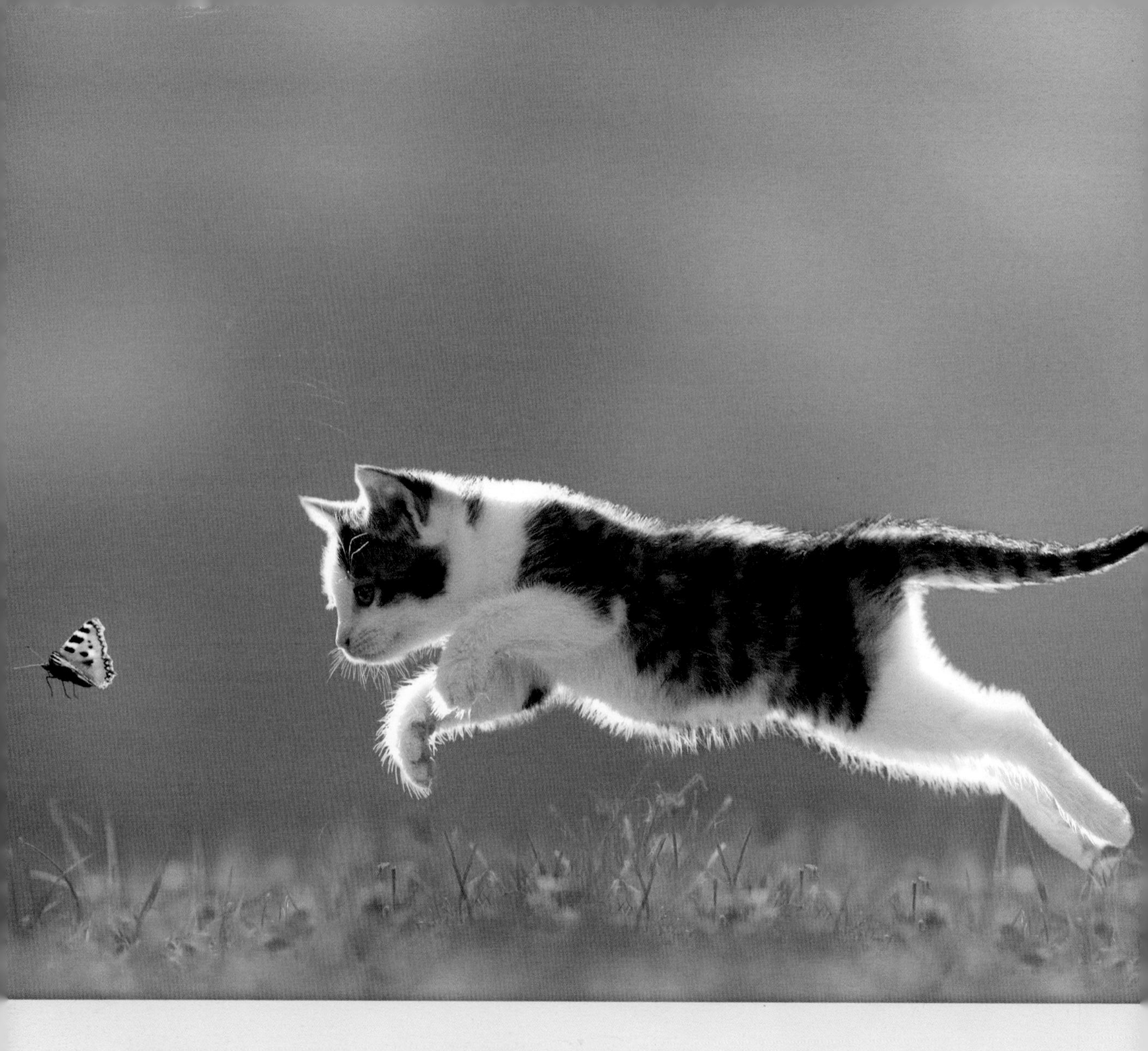

Can cat run?
Cat can run.

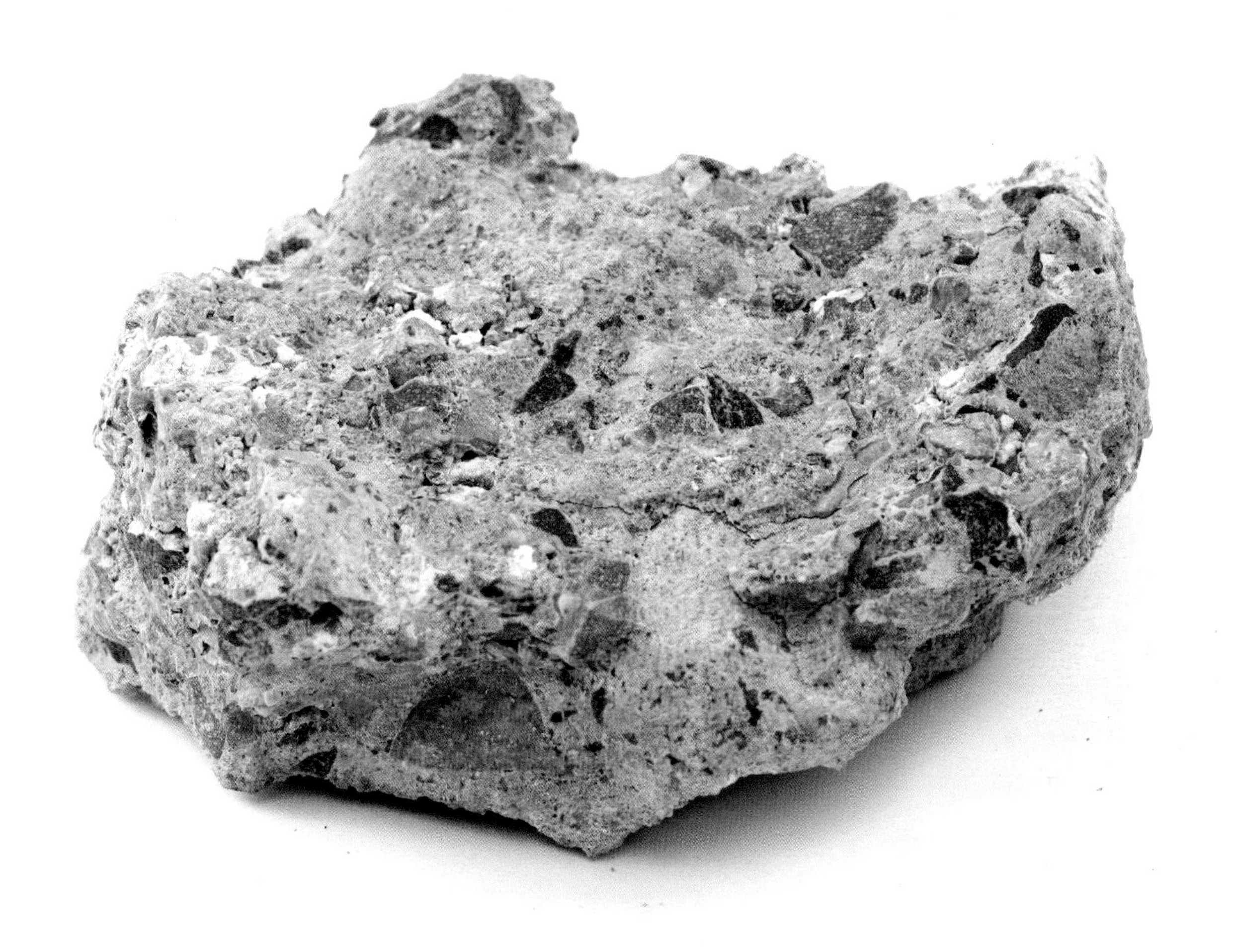

Can rock run?
No, rock can not run.

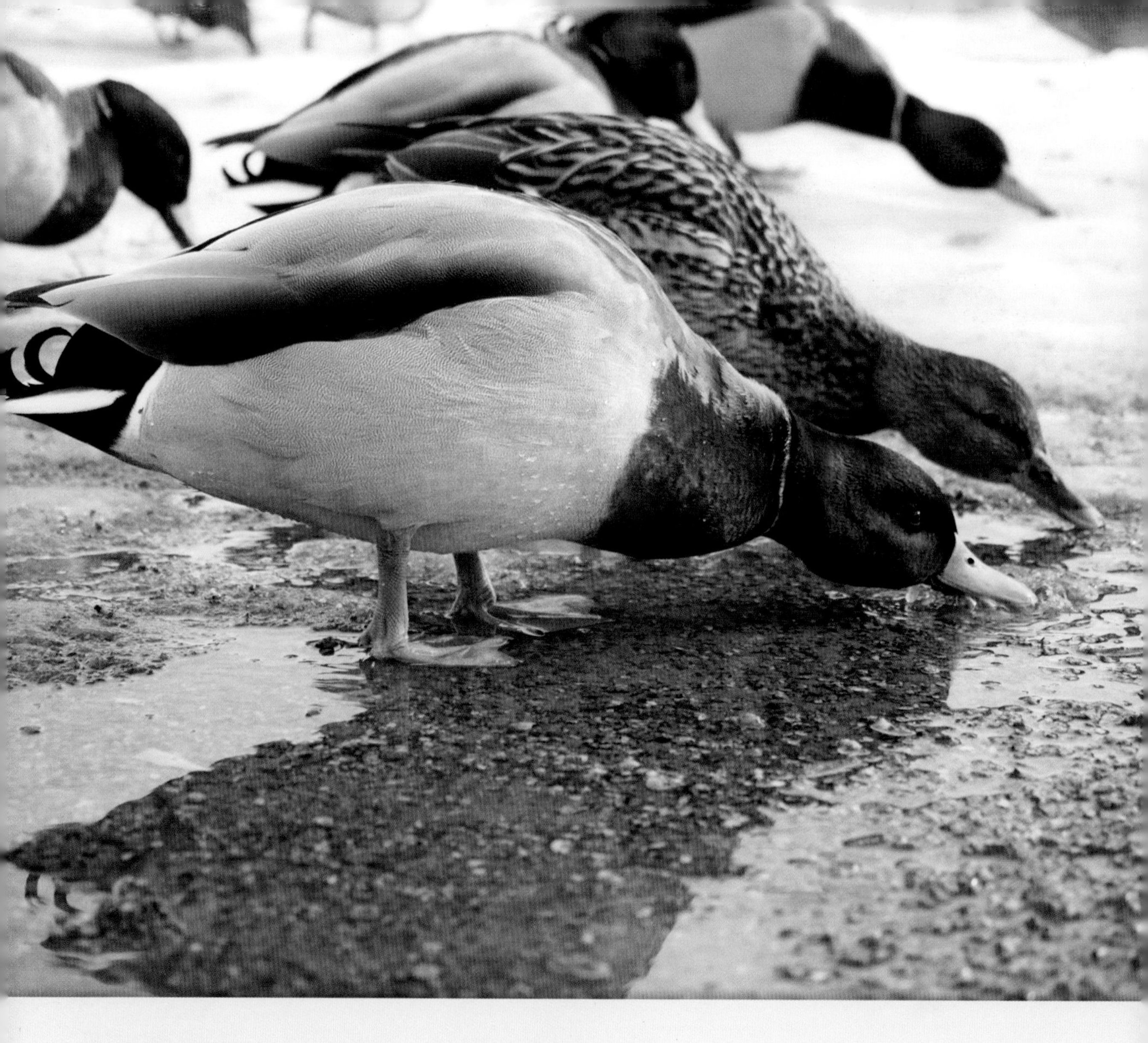

Can duck peck?
Duck can peck.

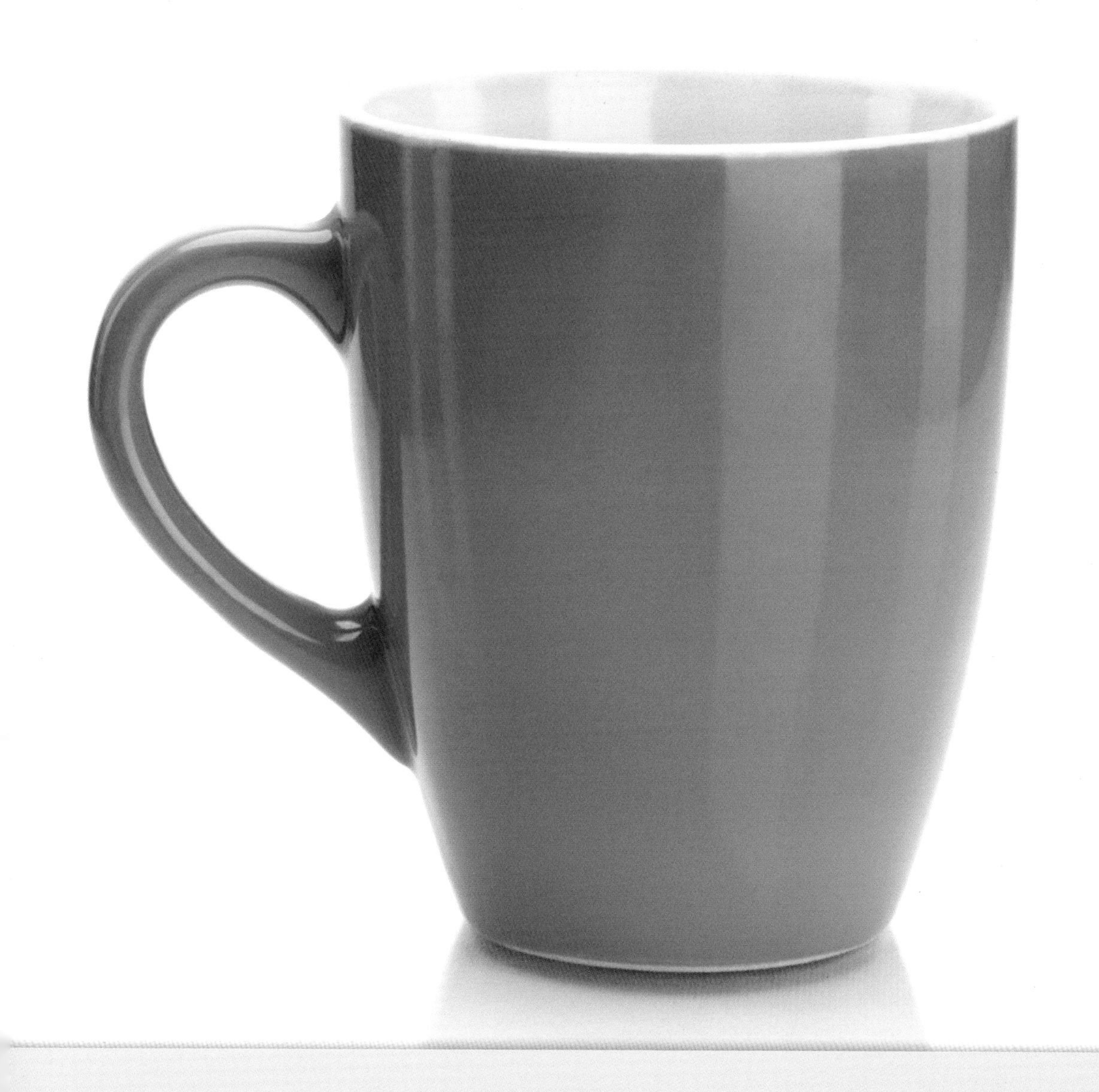

Can mug peck?
No, mug can not peck.

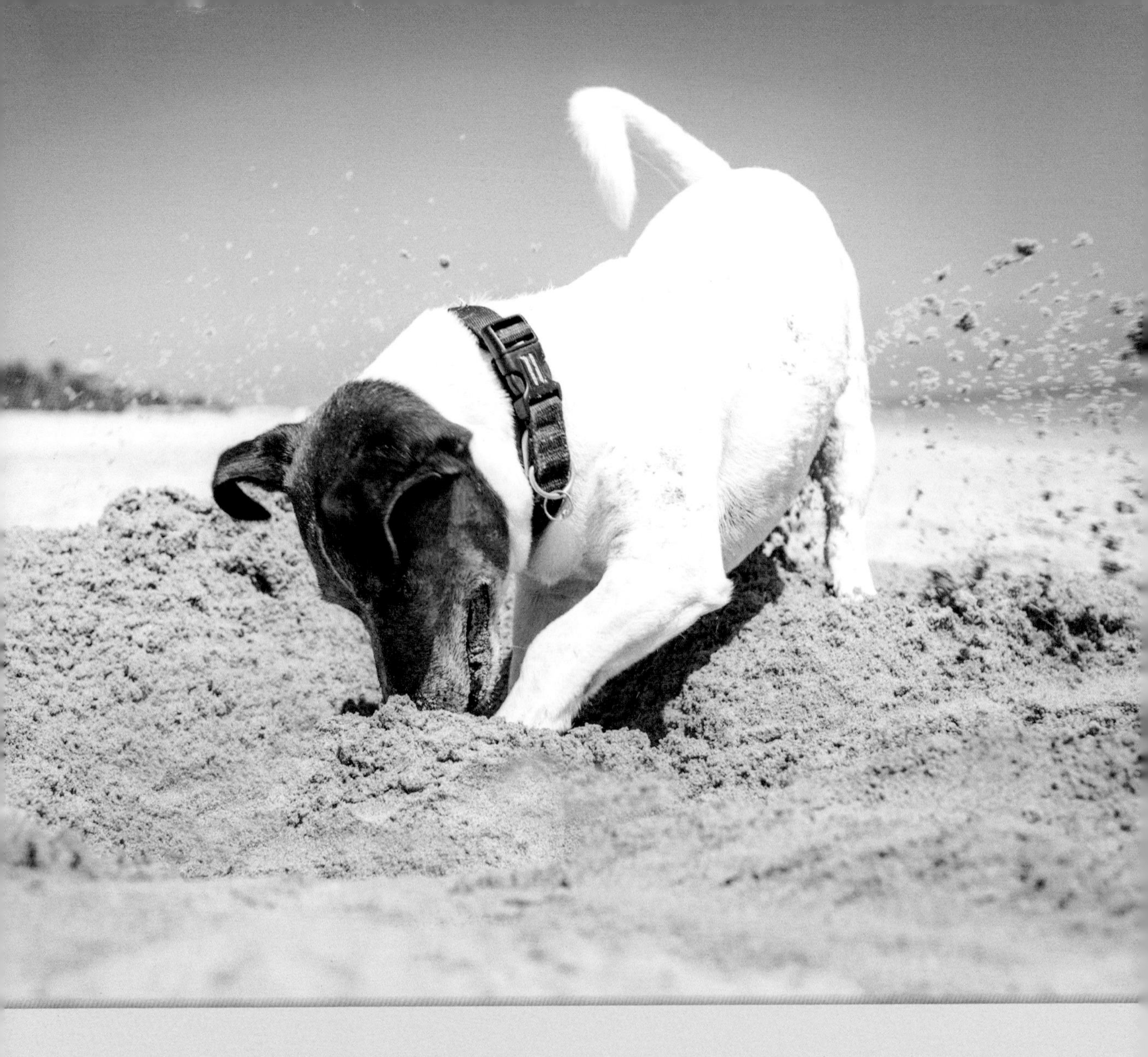

Can pup dig?
Pup can dig.

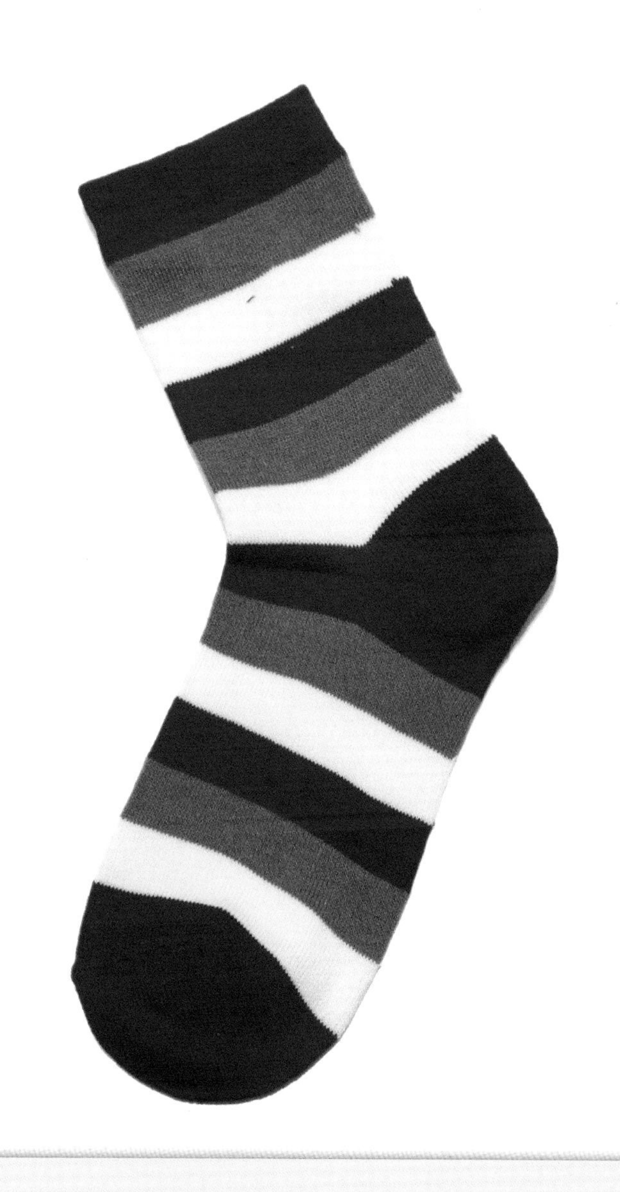

Can sock dig?

No, sock can not dig.

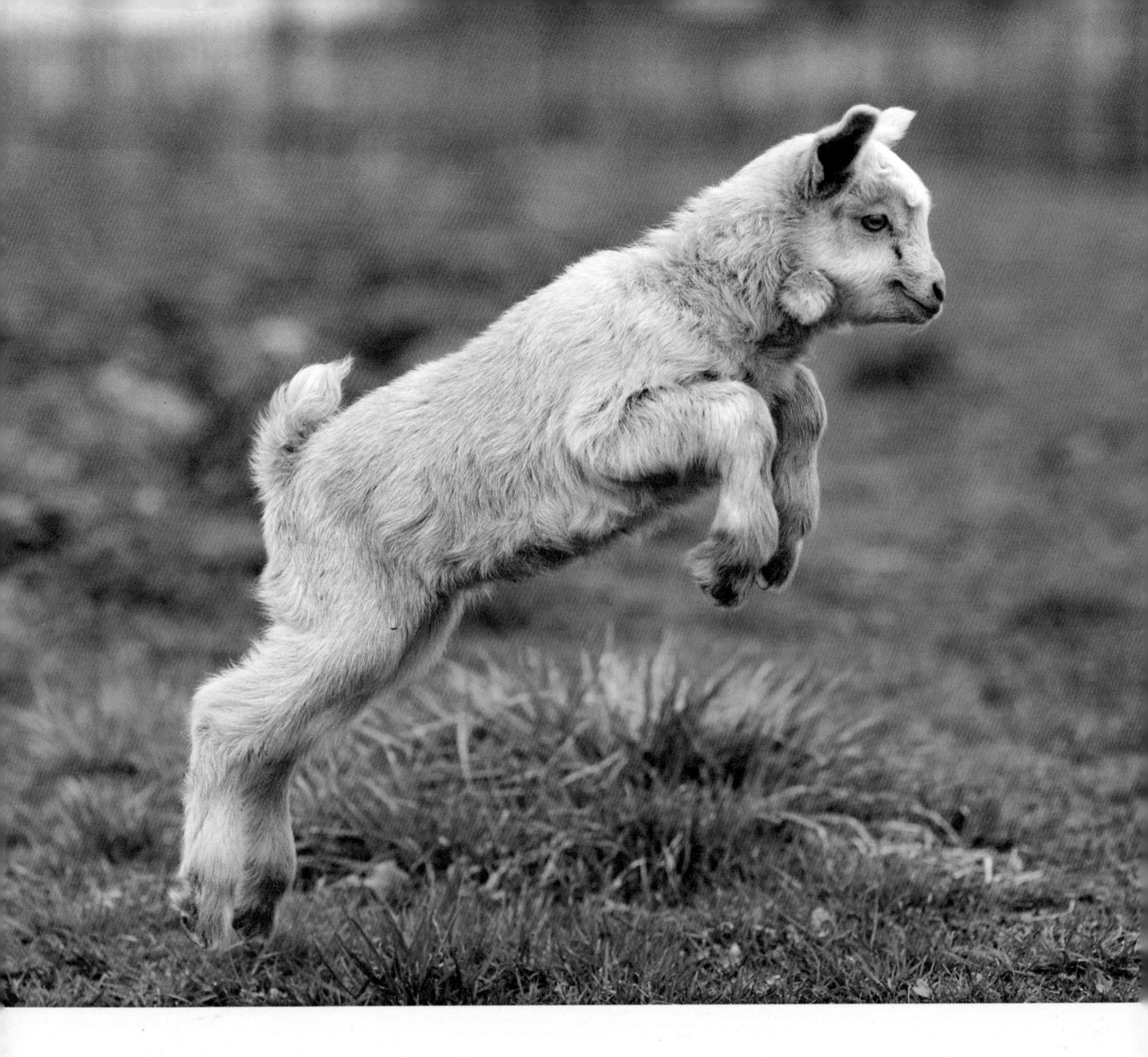

Can the kid go?
The kid can go.